Danny the
Water Dragon

by **Felicity Pulman**

illustrated by **Brenda Cantell**

T

The Characters

That's me.

Danny
The water dragon

The Setting

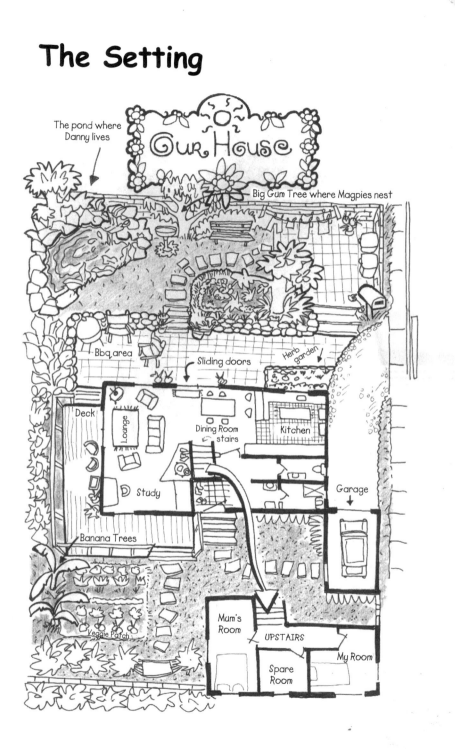

The pond where Danny lives

Our House

Big Gum Tree where Magpies nest

Bbq area

Sliding doors

Herb garden

Deck

Lounge

Dining Room

stairs

Kitchen

Study

Garage

Banana Trees

Veggie Patch

Mum's Room

UPSTAIRS

My Room

Spare Room

CONTENTS

Chapter 1
Danny lives in our
garden 2

Chapter 2
Danny looks like
a dragon 6

Chapter 3
Danny's reptile family . . 12

Chapter 4
Danny is the boss 18

Chapter 5
Be careful —
dragons bite! 26

Chapter 6
A dragon's lunch 32

Chapter 7
Dragons can swim 44

Chapter 8
A garden full of
animals 50

CHAPTER 1

Danny lives in our garden

A family of Eastern Water Dragons lives next to the pond in our garden. Before I continue, I should explain that we live in Sydney, on the east coast of Australia. Danny is the biggest dragon. From his snout to the tip of his tail, he is nearly a metre long.

He visits me every day. He bangs his
head against the glass doors of our dining
room. It looks as if he wants to come
inside and be a house dragon instead of
a garden dragon.

My Project on Water Dragons

Where They Live

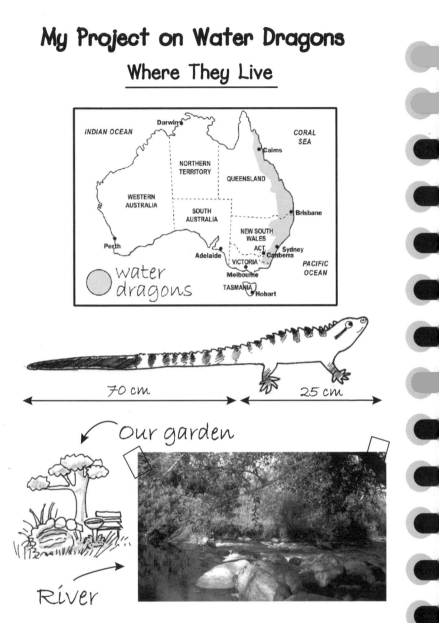

water dragons

70 cm

25 cm

Our garden

River

Physignathus lesueurii, the water dragon, is one of the largest dragons in Australia. They live near creeks, streams and rivers.

They are sometimes found near the beach, living on algae and crabs. The water dragon is sometimes called a 'salamander' by mistake.

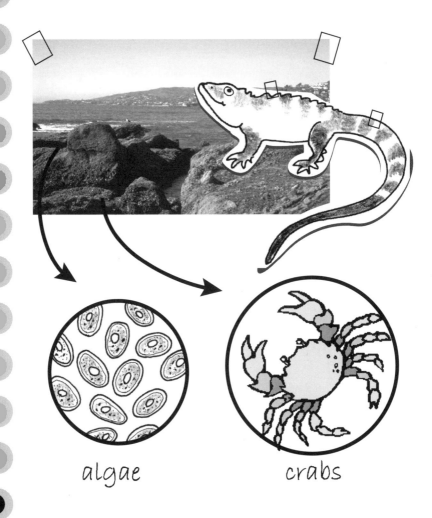

algae

crabs

Danny looks like a dragon

Danny is a very handsome dragon.
He has a creamy grey head with wide
black stripes on either side.

He has a wide mouth, tiny nostrils and dark eyes. He has a striped black and grey tail and back.

His skin is rough and scaly, and he has
a row of sharp spines down his back.
He has a dark grey belly, which sometimes
flushes bright red.

He has five claws on each arm and leg. The front claws are quite short. There are two short claws on each back leg, plus a mid-length claw and two long claws in the middle, which help him hold on when he climbs.

Types of Water Dragons

Water dragons belong to the lizard family Agamidae. There are 64 species of dragon lizards in Australia.

thorny devil

bearded dragon

frilled lizard

The species include the frilled lizard,
the bearded dragon and the really
weird Moloch horridus, the thorny devil
or desert dragon, which is blotched in
the colours of the desert and covered
with spiky 'thorns'.

CHAPTER 3

Danny's reptile family

Danny is the grandpa of the family in our garden. He has many children and grandchildren. The smallest dragon is only about 10cm long.

We have no cats or dogs, so our dragons live in safety. If there are no predators around, a water dragon can live for over 15 years.

Danny and his family disappear from the garden during the cold winter months.
I am not sure where they go, but they come back as soon as it starts to warm up again.

During summer, the water dragons shed their skins and grow new ones — just like snakes.

How Water Dragons Have Babies

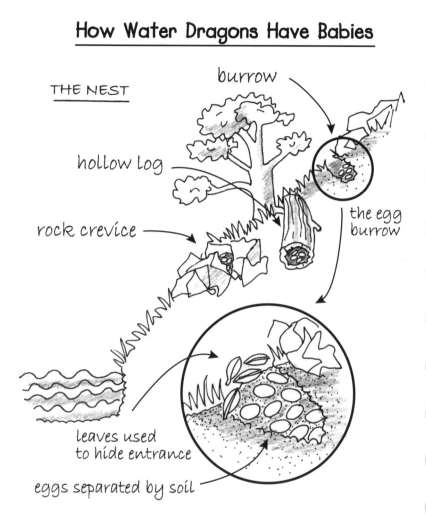

THE NEST

burrow

hollow log

rock crevice

the egg burrow

leaves used to hide entrance

eggs separated by soil

Water dragons are reptiles. They lay their eggs in burrows, rocks or hollow logs away from the water, so there is no chance of the nest being flooded. They lay between 6 to 18 eggs at a time.

The water dragon can use its snout to roll eggs into the egg chamber. Sometimes the water dragon will pick up the egg and carry it in its mouth. Water dragons do not reproduce (have babies) until they are several years old.

the eggs hatch in
70-120 days

CHAPTER 4

Danny is the boss

Bang! Danny's head hits the glass sliding door.

"Good morning, Danny."

He bobs his head up and down and flicks his tail from side to side.

Bang! He headbutts the door again. At first, I thought he was trying to get inside, but now I know what he really wants.

He wants a fight. He wants to fight the big dragon that he can see reflected in the glass.

Danny thinks the big dragon is his enemy. He wants to show him who is boss around here.

Sometimes Danny does press-ups. He hunches his back and pushes up and down on his legs. He looks quite funny but the other dragons find him really scary.

Bang! I open the glass door, so he can't see himself anymore.

This Is Danny's Territory

Water dragons are fiercely territorial.
They keep other males out of their area.

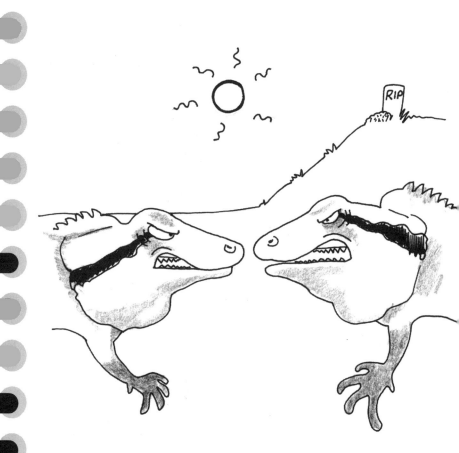

Adult males can fight each other to
the death.

Be careful — dragons bite!

As soon as I open the door, I slide the screen across. If I am not quick enough, or if I forget, Danny runs inside to see what a house looks like.

I used to get very excited when he came inside. I would try to chase him out, and he would race up and down the stairs looking for a door.

"Don't be silly, Danny. You are a garden dragon, not a house dragon. Go outside."

Now I know that if I move quietly, and don't frighten him, he will run outside again. He is quite tame now, which means I can get close to him. But I don't get too close. Danny can bite.

Be Careful!

Water dragons have a deep and nasty bite. Don't get too close to them.

WARNING
Don't touch the
Water Dragons.

They Bite

!

A dragon's lunch

One day I watched Danny hunt a green grasshopper. He stalked it for a while, then pounced on it.

He looked very pleased with himself as
he munched it.

Sometimes Danny eats fruit. He really likes grapes, and bobs his head up and down after he has finished his feast.

Once upon a time, we used to have lots of frogs living in our pond.

We watched their eggs hatch into tadpoles.

The frogs croaked a chorus to us every night. They were especially loud when it rained.

We don't have frogs anymore. We have dragons instead.

The dragons ate the frogs' eggs, the
tadpoles and the baby frogs. So the big
frogs hopped away to find a safer home.

We still have big goldfish living in our pond.

The dragons don't eat the adult goldfish
but I think they eat the babies.

What Water Dragons Eat

Adult water dragons are omnivorous.
They feed on insects, small reptiles
and animals, and water creatures.

spider

fish

grasshopper

frog

small lizards

cicada

They also eat fruits and berries.

berries

figs

berries

flowers

strawberries

Dragons can swim

All water dragons live near water. Danny and his family like to take showers in the waterfall that splashes from bowl to bowl at the side of the pond.

Then they stretch out in the sun.

When people come close, they jump into
the pond. They like to keep their snouts
above water so they can breathe and
watch what is going on.

When in danger, the water dragons move very fast. If they are not close enough to jump into the water, they run away or climb straight up a wall or a tree.

Escaping from Predators

A dragon's heartbeat slows down when it dives into the water. Dragons can stay under water for over an hour. This can help them escape from predators.

PREDATOR

'Ralph'
from no. 4

PREDATOR

'Gloria'
Mrs Rosetti's cat

PREDATOR

'Jimmy'
Mr Watson
at no. 8

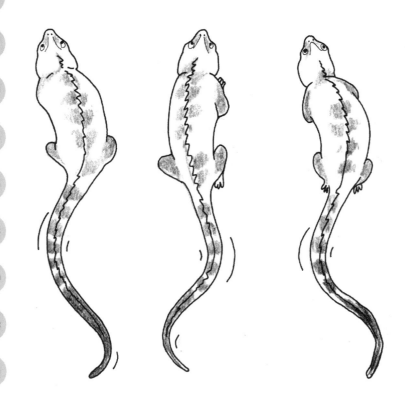

Water dragons are powerful swimmers.
The water dragon tucks its arms and
legs against its body and pushes itself
through the water with its tail.

CHAPTER 8

A garden full of animals

Many creatures live in our garden.

Some are quite small, like butterflies, millipedes, geckos and small lizards that shed their tails when they're caught.

A fat blue-tongued lizard lives under the rubbish bin on our balcony. He comes out when the sun shines and flicks his long, blue tongue, trying to catch insects.

Possums hiss in the night and rustle through the trees. They are heading for the banana palms at the back of the house, hoping to find a bunch of ripe bananas for a feast.

Cackles of kookaburras, colourful rosellas and screeching cockatoos all visit our garden.

Black and white magpies nest in a gumtree every year. We watch the baby birds grow and learn how to fly.

Life in Our Garden

A garden is a little environment.

Our garden's food chain

(look out for the cat next door!
She seems to eat everything.)

Animals live in the soil, in the pond and in the trees. There are also other animals that only visit.

GLOSSARY

algae
microscopic plant cells

chorus
voices or noises together

hunches
crouches forward
with shoulders up

omnivorous
plant eating and meat eating

predators
animals that hunt other
animals for food

snout
an animal's nose

stalked
quietly followed every movement

territorial
an animal that defends
its own area

Felicity Pulman

What is your favourite thing?

Music.

What do you like about yourself?

My imagination. I really like making up stories.

Why did the cow jump over the moon?

To see the stars on the other side.

What is your best midnight snack?

Chocolate. Lots. Not just at midnight either!

Brenda Cantell

What is your favourite thing?

My husband Ben (of course) and my denim jacket.

What do you like about yourself?

I laugh (a lot), sometimes at myself and often when I shouldn't.

Why did the cow jump over the moon?

For the sheer thrill of it, and the night breeze through her ears.

What is your best midnight snack?

Ambrosia Devon Cream Custard, served chilled.